Tall-Tale Math
Book 2: Pre-Algebra

Written by Elizabeth Hoover
Cover Design and Illustrations by Koryn Agnello

Printed in the U.S.A.

EDUCATIONAL IMPRESSIONS, INC.
Hawthorne, New Jersey 07507

ISBN 1-56644-057-2

EDUCATIONAL IMPRESSIONS, INC.
Hawthorne, New Jersey 07507

Contents

An Introduction to Pre-Algebra

Mathematics is much more than numbers, formulas, and theories. It is a vital, fascinating part of our daily lives. Whether we're hitting a grand slam, making chocolate chip cookies, or reading a science-fiction novel, math helps us understand and enjoy the world in which we live.

The Math Clues Series is a comprehensive resource that empowers students by helping them understand and utilize the fundamentals of mathematics. Highly creative story problems spark curiosity and help students appreciate math as a powerful tool for solving real-life questions.

In Part 2 of the series, *Pre-Algebra*, students will explore the fundamental principles of algebra, including equations, variables, algebraic expressions, and probabilities.

Pre-Algebra is divided into three useful sections:

Review Sheets contain easy-to-understand definitions and examples that clearly explain particular concepts, such as "Equations." In addition to providing valuable practice exercises, the sheets can also serve as handy reference guides.

Skill-Builder Sheets present intriguing story problems that use humor, creativity, and mystery to engage students. Each sheet covers a specific concept, which is clearly labeled at the top of the page.

Extra-Practice Sheets are designed to add an additional challenge for students who have mastered the previous sheets. In addition to the basic concepts, students must use additional skills, such as measurement conversion, chart analysis, and selection of the most appropriate number form. These sheets give teachers the extra flexibility to tailor lessons based on grade level and ability.

Learning Objectives

Pre-Algebra was designed to help instructors implement the National Council of Teachers of Mathematics Curriculum and Evaluation Standards. Aimed at students in grades 5 through 8, the sheets will help students meet the following specific objectives:

- solving basic equations

- identifying and working with variables

- understanding and working with equations containing fractions

- understanding and working with equations containing parentheses

- understanding and working with equations containing negative and positive integers

- writing algebraic expressions

- writing equations to solve word problems

- writing and solving equations with variables on both sides of the equal sign

- using probability to solve equations

- connecting math to the world outside the classroom

- using investigation and reasoning to solve problems

Educational Impressions, Inc.

Review Sheets

What's an Equation?

An **equation** is a math sentence with an equal sign.

$$x - 3 = 1$$

Most equations contain one or more **variables**, or letters that stand for numbers. In the equation above, x is the variable.

To solve the equation, we must find the number that x represents. This will be the **solution**. When plugged into the equation, the solution will make both sides of the equation equal.

To solve an equation, remember the Golden Rule:
Always perform the opposite operation on both sides of the equation.

In our example, 3 is **subtracted** from x. To perform the opposite operation, we will **add** 3 to both sides of the equation.

$$x - 3 + 3 = 1 + 3$$

On the left, we add -3 to 3 and get zero. Since zero adds no value, we can drop it from our equation. On the right, we add 1 to 3 and get 4. Now our equation looks like this:

$$x = 4$$

When x is by itself on one side of the equal sign, the equation is solved. We can test our solution by plugging it into the original equation.

$$4 - 3 = 1$$

1. Name the variable in the equation below.

    $$y + 7 = 20$$

2. To solve the equation below, what would you add to each side?

    $$x - 1/2 = 10$$

3. Name the opposite operation that should be performed in the equation below.

    $$x - 2 = 5$$

4. Name the opposite operation that should be performed in the equation below.

    $$x - 7 = 9$$

Educational Impressions, Inc.

Working With Variables

If a variable is placed next to another quantity, it means the variable and the quantity are being multiplied together.

$2y$ = 2 multiplied by y

A variable multiplied by a quantity is called a **monomial**. Since $y = 1 \times y$, we can replace y with $1y$.

• Monomials with the same variables can be added, subtracted, and multiplied.

$3x + 4x = 7x$

$10y - 5y = 5y$

$4x\,(2x) = 8x^2$

• Monomials with the same variables can be divided by each other. The variables cancel each other out.

$\dfrac{12x}{6x} = 2$

• Variables, monomials, and other quantities in the equation can be multiplied together.

$2x\,(5) = 10x$

$1/2\,(6x) = 3x$

$3x\,(4y) = 12xy$

• Variables, monomials, and other quantities in the equation can be divided by each other.

$\dfrac{4x}{2} = 2x$ $\qquad$ $\dfrac{30}{5x} = \dfrac{6}{x}$ $\qquad$ $\dfrac{8x}{4y} = \dfrac{2x}{y}$

• Variables, monomials, and other quantities **cannot** be combined with addition or subtraction.

$4 + 8y \neq 12y$

$10 - 3x \neq 7x$

Solve each of the problems below.

1. $12x - 4x =$

2. $14x + 17x =$

3. $5x\,(3x) =$

4. $32x/8x =$

5. $4x\,(13) =$

6. $2/3\,(6x) =$

7. $15x/3 =$

8. $40/2x =$

Using Addition to Solve Equations

Always perform the opposite operation on both sides of the equation.

$$x - 4 = 3$$

In this example, 4 is **subtracted** from x. To perform the opposite operation, we will **add** 4 to both sides of the equation.

$$x - 4 + 4 = 3 + 4$$

On the left, we add -4 to 4 and get zero. Since zero adds no value, we can drop it from our equation. On the right, we add 3 to 4 and get 7.

$$x = 7$$

We can test our solution by plugging it into the original equation.

$$7 - 4 = 3$$

Use the opposite operation to solve the equations below. (HINT: In each case, the opposite operation will be addition.)

1. $c - 34 = 21$ $c =$

2. $y - .5 = 2.5$ $y =$

3. $s - 0 = 12$ $s =$

4. $z - 2/3 = 1/3$ $z =$

5. $m - 9 = 0$ $m =$

Educational Impressions, Inc.

Using Subtraction to Solve Equations

Always perform the opposite operation on both sides of the equation.

$x + 6 = 10$

Since 6 is **added** to x, we will **subtract** 6 from both sides of the equation.

$x + 6 - \mathbf{6} = 10 - \mathbf{6}$

On the left, we subtract 6 from 6 and get zero. Since zero adds no value, we can drop it from our equation. On the right, we subtract 6 from 10 and get 4.

$x = 4$

We can test our solution by plugging it into the original equation.

$4 + 6 = 10$

Use the opposite operation to solve the equations below. (HINT: In each case, the opposite operation will be subtraction.)

1. $j + 35 = 90$ $j =$

2. $x + 12 = 18$ $x =$

3. $k + 1.5 = 3.8$ $k =$

4. $y + 1/4 = 3/4$ $y =$

5. $m + 23 = 0$ $m =$

Using Division to Solve Equations

Always perform the opposite operation on both sides of the equation.

$$2 \times y = 4$$

"$2 \times y$" is another way of writing "2 multiplied by y." Since 2 is **multiplied** by y, we will **divide** both sides of the equation by 2.

$$\frac{2y}{2} = \frac{4}{2}$$

On the left, we divide $2y$ by 2 and get $1y$. Since $1y = y$, we can drop the 1 from our equation. On the right, we divide 4 by 2 and get 2.

$$y = 2$$

We can test our solution by plugging it into the original equation.

$$2\,(2) = 4$$

Use the opposite operation to solve the equations below. (HINT: In each case, the opposite operation will be division.)

1. $4z = 12$ $z =$

2. $-2m = -12$ $m =$

3. $1.5k = 6$ $k =$

4. $23y = 184$ $y =$

5. $1/6c = 3$ $c =$

Educational Impressions, Inc.

Using Multiplication to Solve Equations

Always perform the opposite operation on both sides of the equation.

$$\frac{y}{6} = 2$$

Since y is **divided** by 6, we will **multiply** each side by 6.

$$\frac{y}{6}(6) = 2\ (6)$$

On the left, we multiply y/6 by 6 and get 6y/6. On the right, we multiply 2 by 6 and get 12.

$$\frac{6y}{6} = 12$$

On the left, we have 6 over 6, which equals 1. The sixes can be dropped from the equation.

$$y = 12$$

We can test our solution by plugging it into the original equation.

$$\frac{12}{6} = 2$$

Use the opposite operation to solve the equations below. (HINT: In each case, the opposite operation will be multiplication.)

1. $12/z = 4$ $z =$

2. $68/x = 17$ $x =$

3. $-30/c = -6$ $c =$

4. $8/b = 8$ $b =$

5. $4/x = 1$ $x =$

Combining Like Terms

Many equations are easier to solve if we start by combining like terms. For example, we can combine all of the whole numbers in the equation, or all of the fractions, or all of the decimals. We can also combine variables and monomials that share the same letter, like y, $3y$, and $6y$.

Let's combine like terms to solve the equation below.

$2x + 4x = 14 - 2$

First, we will combine the whole numbers in the problem.

$2x + 4x = \mathbf{14 - 2}$
$2x + 4x = \mathbf{12}$

Next, we will combine the monomials containing the variable x.

$\mathbf{2x + 4x} = 12$
$\mathbf{6x} = 12$

Now the equation is easier to solve.

$$\frac{6x}{6} = \frac{12}{6}$$

$x = 2$

Simplify each equation by combining like terms. Then solve the equations.

1. $3x + 9x = 13 - 1$

2. $10 - 2 = 3c - c$

3. $4y + y + 3y = 10 + 22$

4. $6z + 5 - 4 = 7 + 6$

5. $12n - 9n = 38 - 2$

6. $4 - 6 = 2y - 8y$

7. $1/2x + 2/4x = 16 + 1/2$

8. $3.5m - 1.75m = 6.5 + 2.25$

Educational Impressions, Inc.

Equations with Fractions

To solve equations containing fractions and mixed numbers, we must remember what we know about adding, subtracting, multiplying, and dividing fractions.

To **add** fractions with the same denominators, we add the numerators. The denominator stays the same.

$$1/4 + 2/4 = 3/4$$

To **add** fractions with different denominators, we must find a common denominator and add the numerators.

$$1/5 + 1/3 = 3/15 + 5/15 = 8/15$$

To **subtract** fractions with the same denominators, we subtract the numerators. The denominator stays the same.

$$3/5 - 1/5 = 2/5$$

To **subtract** fractions with different denominators, we must find a common denominator and subtract the numerators.

$$1/2 - 1/5 = 5/10 - 2/10 = 3/10$$

To **multiply** fractions, we multiply the numerators together, then multiply the denominators together.

$$2/3 \times 3/4 = 6/12 = 1/2$$

To **divide** fractions, we flip the second fraction upside down and treat the problem as if it were a multiplication problem.

$$1/2 \div 2/3 = 1/2 \times 3/2 = 3/4$$

Using multiplication, we can combine fractions and variables.

$$\frac{1}{4}y = \frac{1}{4} \times \frac{y}{1} = \frac{y}{4}$$

Solve the problems below. Reduce answers to their lowest terms.

1. $1/4 + 1/3 =$

2. $4/5 - 1/2 =$

3. $1/6 \times 2/5 =$

4. $2/9 \div 1/3 =$

5. $2\ 1/3 + 1/3 =$

6. $3\ 1/2 - 1\ 1/6 =$

7. $1/9 \times 3 =$

8. $3/4 \times 6 =$

Extra Review: Equations with Fractions

Find the value of x in the following equations.

1. $1/2x + 3 = 5$

2. $x + 1/3 = 5/6$

3. $x - 7/8 = 1/4$

4. $x + 2/5 = 7/10$

5. $1/4x + 5 = 10$

6. $3/4 - x = 11/20$

7. $x - 1/2 + 1/4 = 2\ 3/4$

8. $2x = 2\ 1/2$

9. $1/8 = 1/3x$

10. $x + 3/5 = 9/10$

Educational Impressions, Inc.

Equations with Parentheses

Many equations contain parentheses.

$4 (2a + 1) = 28$

We can simplify these equations by multiplying the number outside the parentheses by each number inside the parentheses. This is called the **Distributive Law of Multiplication over Addition**. It says that $x (y + z) = xy + xz$.

$4 (2a + 1) = 28$

$(4) (2a) + (4) (1) = 28$

$8a + 4 = 28$

Now the equation is easier to solve.

$8a + 4 - \textbf{4} = 28 - \textbf{4}$

$\dfrac{8a}{8} = \dfrac{24}{8}$

$a = 3$

Simplify the expressions below using the Distributive Law of Multiplication over Addition.

1. $4 (x - 5)$

2. $3 (2x + 7)$

3. $7 (3c + 13)$

4. $1/2 (2a + 8a)$

5. $1.2 (2.4z + 4)$

6. $4 (6y - 2)$

7. $8 (5 - 2x)$

8. $1/4 (4b - 1/2)$

Extra Review: Equations with Parentheses

Find the value of x in the following equations.

1. $5(x + 3) = 25$

2. $6(11 - x) = 42$

3. $4(x + 12) = 2(20 + 22)$

4. $1/2(x - 7) = -2$

5. $2/3(9 - x) = -3 + 3$

6. $1.5(x - 8) = 4.5$

7. $5x(3) = 67.5$

8. $1/2(x + 12) = 5(1.8)$

9. $3(0 - x) = -15$

10. $1\ 1/2(x + 4) = 6\ 3/4$

Educational Impressions, Inc.

Equations with Positive and Negative Numbers

When equations contain positive and negative numbers, it helps to remember a few rules.

To **add** positive and negative numbers:

If the signs are the same, add the numbers and keep the sign.

$4 + 2 = 6$

$-4 + (-2) = -6$

If the signs are opposite, find the difference and keep the sign of the larger number.

$-5 + 2 = -3$

$7 + (-6) = 1$

To **subtract** a positive or negative number from another number, simply add the opposite.

$5 - (-3) = 5 + (+3) = 8$

To **multiply and divide** positive and negative numbers, use the rules below.

positive × positive = positive	$4 \times 2 = 8$	positive ÷ positive = positive	$8 \div 2 = 4$
positive × negative = negative	$4 \times -2 = -8$	positive ÷ negative = negative	$8 \div (-2) = -4$
negative × positive = negative	$-4 \times 2 = -8$	negative ÷ positive = negative	$-8 \div 2 = -4$
negative × negative = positive	$-4 \times -2 = 8$	negative ÷ negative = positive	$-8 \div (-2) = 4$

Solve the problems below.

1. $-14 + (-7) =$

2. $12 - (-4) =$

3. $4 \times (-8) =$

4. $10 + (-4) =$

5. $15 \div (-3) =$

6. $-4 \times (-15) =$

7. $10 + (-22) =$

8. $-36 \div (-12) =$

9. $-13 \times 7 =$

10. $-21 + 8 =$

Extra Review: Equations with Positive and Negative Numbers

Find the value of x in the following equations.

1. $-6x = -72$

2. $5x - 6x = -8$

3. $10 - x = -55$

4. $-1/2x + 3 = 0$

5. $x - 9.3 = -3.8$

6. $x - 7/8 = -3/8$

7. $x + 2/5 = -1/10$

8. $12 - x = -4.5$

9. $4x\ (2) = -1.6\ (5)$

10. $-x - 4 = 4.5\ (-2)$

Educational Impressions, Inc.

Writing Algebraic Expressions

An **algebraic expression** uses numbers and symbols to describe a quantity. Below are some examples.

Phrase	**Algebraic Expression**
12 decreased by 2	$12 - 2$
5 more than 3	$3 + 5$
7 less than x	$x - 7$
the sum of 8 and 4	$8 + 4$
the product of 2 and 3	2×3
4 more than 3 times x	$3x + 4$
5 times x, increased by 9	$5x + 9$
2 less than 6 times a number, n	$6n - 2$

Write each phrase below as an algebraic expression.

1. 5 increased by 4

2. 6 more than 2

3. 12 decreased by 6

4. 3 more than -8

5. the product of 4 and -2

6. the sum of x and 5

7. 8 times y, increased by 9

8. twice x, decreased by 3

9. x more than 5 times z

10. 18 less than half of y

Extra Review: Writing Algebraic Expressions

Write an algebraic expression for each of the following word problems. The first one has been done for you.

1. Geri is 12 years old. How old will she be in x years?

   Answer: $12 + x$

2. The sum of two numbers is 24. The larger number is y. What is the smaller number?

3. Phil has 6 more sweatshirts than he has caps. If he has m sweatshirts, how many caps does he have?

4. Dr. Booth was n years old 20 years ago. How old is he now?

5. The sum of John's math test score and Pete's math test score is 168. If John scored y points, what did Pete score?

6. Chef Patooie has 6 times more tomatoes than he has carrots. If he has x carrots, how many tomatoes does he have?

7. Jeb has 5 more skateboards than the sum of his baseballs and footballs. If he has b baseballs and f footballs, how many skateboards does he have?

8. The height of a building is half the width of its base. If the height is h, what is the width of its base?

Educational Impressions, Inc.

Writing Equations for Word Problems

A word problem can be easier to solve if we change the words into an equation. The key to an equation is the equal sign. When we see the word "is" in a word problem, we can replace it with an equal sign in the equation.

Phrase	**Algebraic Expression**
the sum of 6 and 4 **is** 10	$6 + 4 = 10$
5 less than n **is** 12	$n - 5 = 12$
the product of 3 and 4 **is** 12	$3 \times 4 = 12$

Write an equation for each word problem below.

1. The sum of 31 and a number, n, is 48.

2. A number, y, subtracted from 89 is 67.

3. Five more than half the number n is 21.

4. Mike's age, m, is three times Saul's age, s.

5. Nina's height, n, is 3 inches less than Brett's height, b.

6. Eleven increased by half a number, n, is 77.

7. Forty percent of a number, y, is 48.

8. The sum of 4 and 20 multiplied by a number, z, is 144.

Extra Review: Writing Equations for Word Problems

Write an equation for each question, then solve the equation.

1. A number, *n*, subtracted from 21 results in a difference of 14. What number is *n*?

2. Twelve more than twice a number, *x*, is 102. What number is *x*?

3. Four increased by one-third of a number, *y*, is 34. What number is *y*?

4. Fifteen percent of a number, *z*, is 24. What number is *z*?

5. Thirty is triple the sum of 4 and a number, *c*. What number is *c*?

6. A number, *y*, divided by 14 results in a quotient of 6. What number is *y*?

7. The sum of 54 and a number, *m*, is 54. What number is *m*?

8. Five increased by one-fourth of a number, *j*, is 21. What number is *j*?

Educational Impressions, Inc.

Equations with Variables on Both Sides

Some equations have variables on both sides of the equal sign.

$$x + 12 = 5x$$

As always, we use the opposite operations to solve the equation.

$$\begin{aligned} x + 12 &= 5x \\ -x &\quad -x \\ 12 &= 4x \\ \frac{12}{4} &= \frac{4x}{4} \\ 3 &= x \end{aligned}$$

Some word problems must be changed to equations with variables on both sides of the equal sign. It helps to remember that "is" must be replaced with an equal sign.

Five more than x is 3 times x.

$$x + 5 = 3x$$

Write an equation for each word problem. (HINT: All equations will have a variable on both sides.)

1. One more than a number, m, is four times m divided in half.

2. Four times a number, x, is 2 less than x.

3. Three times a number, k, is 12 less than twice the number.

4. One-half more than a number, r, is 6 times the number.

5. The sum of 32 and a number, c, is half of c.

6. A number, n, is one-third the sum of n and 18.

7. Twice a number, j, is 3 more than triple the number.

8. Half a number, b, is 10 less than twice the number.

Extra Review: Equations with Variables on Both Sides

Write an equation for each word problem, then solve the equation. (HINT: All equations will have a variable on both sides.)

1. Half a number, *k*, is 5 more than triple the number. What number is *k*?

2. A number, *d*, is one-third the sum of *d* and 36. What number is *d*?

3. Twice a number, *n*, is 5 less than triple the number. What is the number?

4. Half a number, *y*, is 18 less than twice the number. What number is *y*?

5. The sum of 16 and a number, *c*, is half of *c*. What number is *c*?

6. Three times a number, *x*, is 12 less than *x*. What number is *x*?

7. Twelve more than a number, *m*, is four times *m* divided in half. What number is *m*?

8. One-half more than a number, *z*, is three times the number. What number is *z*?

Educational Impressions, Inc.

Using Proportion to Solve Equations

Sometimes we can solve a problem by writing a proportion. A **proportion** is a way to compare two quantities.

Let's say there are 25 fish in a pond. Only 5 of the fish have purple stripes. We want to know what percentage of the fish have purple stripes.

For the first quantity, we place 5 over 25. This is one way to show how many fish have purple stripes.

$$\frac{5}{25} =$$

Remember that percentage means "out of 100." Since the second quantity is an unknown percentage, we place x over 100.

$$\frac{5}{25} = \frac{x}{100}$$

We can find the value of x by cross multiplying.

$$\frac{5}{25} \diagdown\kern-1.2em\diagup \frac{x}{100}$$

$$25x = 5\,(100)$$

$$\frac{25x}{25} = \frac{500}{25}$$

$$x = 20$$

Use cross multiplication to solve the proportions below.

1. $\dfrac{z}{6} = \dfrac{4}{24}$ $z =$

2. $\dfrac{2}{3} = \dfrac{8}{k}$ $k =$

3. $\dfrac{-4}{8} = \dfrac{5}{-y}$ $y =$

4. $\dfrac{2a}{6} = \dfrac{12}{9}$ $a =$

5. $\dfrac{11}{-3} = \dfrac{44}{-x}$ $x =$

Extra Review: Using Proportion to Solve Equations

Write an proportion to solve each word problem below, then use the proportions to answer the questions.

1. There are 38 students in a science class. Only 19 of the students are girls. What percentage of the students are girls?

2. There are 55 sailboats in a race. Twenty-two of the boats have white sails. What percentage of the boats do not have white sails?

3. A fourth of Mr. White's candy bars are covered with chocolate. The rest of the candy bars are covered with caramel. What percentage of the candy bars are covered with caramel?

4. Last year, Jacob won 4 out of 12 categories on Field Day. This year, he won the same percentage of categories. However, there were 18 categories this year. How many categories did Jacob win this year?

5. Sarah and Kate have the same percentage of females in their families. Sarah has 2 females in her family and a total of 6 family members. Kate has 3 females in her family. How many family members does Kate have?

6. At the game, Todd made 60% of the baskets he attempted. He made 51 baskets. How many baskets did he attempt?

Educational Impressions, Inc.

Extra Review: Solving Equations

Solve each equation for *y*, then check your answers.

1. $2y = 8$ $y =$

2. $4 + y = -24$ $y =$

3. $-12y = -72$ $y =$

4. $5y = 0$ $y =$

5. $-4.3 + y = 2.8$ $y =$

6. $1/3y = 3/18$ $y =$

7. $8 - y = -1.5$ $y =$

8. $12\ 1/2 - y = 10$ $y =$

9. $-y = -3.9$ $y =$

10. $-72y = 36$ $y =$

Solve each equation for *x*, then check your answers.

11. $5\ (x + 3) = 20$ $x =$

12. $4\ (2 - x) = 8$ $x =$

13. $-6\ (x + 5) = -42$ $x =$

14. $-2\ (x + 3) = 4\ (3 - 1)$ $x =$

15. $2\ (5x) = -15\ (2)$ $x =$

16. $-8\ (2 - x) = 24$ $x =$

17. $1/2\ (3 + x) = 12$ $x =$

18. $-1\ (-4 + 6) = -x$ $x =$

19. $4x + (-8 - 2) = 30$ $x =$

20. $1.5\ (2 - 3x) = -24$ $x =$

Skill-Builder Sheets

Wilheim's Wax Museum
(Using Addition to Solve Equations)

Mr. Wilheim owned the biggest wax museum in the world. It was filled with wax statues of famous people, scary monsters, and amazing animals.

Help Mr. Wilheim with the problems below. Write an equation for each problem, then solve it. When you're done, check your answers.

1. While creating his Frankenstein statue, Mr. Wilheim made a batch of green wax. He molded Frankenstein's head first, using 9 gallons of wax. After that, there were 68 gallons of green wax remaining. How many gallons of green wax did Mr. Wilheim make originally?

2. For his statue of King Kong, Mr. Wilheim made 342 gallons of brown wax. Unfortunately, he burned some of the wax while it was cooking. He was able to save 256 gallons. How many gallons of wax burned?

3. While making a statue of Abraham Lincoln, Mr. Wilheim used the wrong mold for Abe's head. He made a Robin Hood head by mistake. In the process, he wasted 6 1/2 gallons of the Lincoln wax. That left him with 67 1/4 gallons. How much Lincoln wax did he have originally?

4. Mr. Wilheim wanted to make a statue of Queen Elizabeth I for his museum. Based on his research, he knew that the queen had been smaller than Betsy Ross. Mr. Wilheim wrote down the amount of wax used for the Betsy Ross statue. For the queen, he would use .6 gallons less for the arms and 1.5 gallons less for the legs. That meant he would use 39.4 gallons of wax for Queen Elizabeth I. How many gallons did Mr. Wilheim use for Betsy Ross?

Educational Impressions, Inc.

Count Dimula
(Using Addition to Solve Equations)

On a tall, rocky mountain in the land of Flakesylvania stands an old castle. It is the home of Count Dimula, the forgetful vampire.

Help Count Dimula with the problems below. Write an equation for each problem, then solve it. When you're done, check your answers.

1. One day, the Count was doing his laundry. He began by washing 23 undershirts. Unfortunately, the Count forgot that red socks and white undershirts shouldn't be washed together. Only 18 of the undershirts stayed white. The rest turned pink. How many undershirts turned pink?

2. One night, the Count was frightened by a loud storm. He was very afraid of lightning. To get his mind off the storm, he decided to feed the mice in the castle. He knew exactly how many mice lived on each floor. Feeding them was one of his favorite hobbies.

    The Count was concerned when he found only 214 mice on the top floor of the castle. There were 8 mice missing. How many mice were supposed to be on the top floor?

3. Feeling blue about the missing mice, the Count decided to cheer himself up with some left-over tomato soup. Every night, he ate the same amount of tomato soup for dinner. But the poor Count had forgotten to go to the grocery. He was 1 7/8 cans short of his usual amount of soup. He only had 3 1/4 cans of soup in the castle. How much soup did the count usually eat for dinner?

S. S. Rainey
(Using Subtraction to Solve Equations)

Mr. R. Rainey, the richest man in the world, bought a huge ship, the *S.S. Rainey*. He wanted to fill the ship with the most expensive things he could find.

Help Mr. Rainey with his shopping. For each problem, write an equation, then solve it. When you're done, check your answers.

1. Mr. Rainey decided to install some swimming pools on the ship. He wanted some of the pools to have spiral slides. He also wanted 13 of the pools to have no slides. In all, there would be 32 pools on the ship. How many pools were to have spiral slides?

2. Mr. Rainey bought some solid gold anchors for his ship. Soon after, he realized that the anchors weren't heavy enough for the massive *S.S. Rainey*. He bought 6 more anchors, but that still didn't do the trick. Mr. Rainey had to buy 7 more anchors before the ship could be held. In all, it took 32 anchors to do the job. How many anchors did Mr. Rainey buy the first time?

3. Mr. Rainey wanted to buy some sharks to circle his ship in case any burglars decided to steal his stuff. He bought 87 sharks from a well-respected shark farmer. By feeding the sharks fresh fish, Mr. Rainey was able to train them to follow his giant ship. A month later, while he was counting the sharks, Mr. Rainey discovered 212 sharks circling his ship. The fresh fish had attracted other hungry sharks to join those he had bought. How many sharks had joined the original group?

4. For his sleeping chambers, Mr. Rainey wanted to sleep on a giant waterbed filled with sea water. He bought the biggest waterbed he could find, but it still wasn't big enough. He had it modified to hold 40 1/2 more gallons of water, for a total of 82 2/3 gallons. How much water did the original waterbed hold?

Educational Impressions, Inc.

The Crackpot Circus
(Using Subtraction to Solve Equations)

Every year, the Crackpot Circus comes to town. It has better shows, rides, and animals than any other circus around.

Write an equation for each problem, then solve it. When you're done, check your answers.

1. The Crackpot Coaster is the best ride at the circus. Last year, an extra hill was built onto the coaster. It added 30 1/2 yards of track. After the hill was added, the coaster's track was 324 2/3 yards long. How long was the track before the new hill was added?

2. Every night at the circus, Marlo the Magician performs a fantastic magic show. The audience always loves it when Marlo makes his pet monkey, Bibo, rise into the air. At one show, Bibo rose 17 feet into the air. As the audience gasped, Bibo rose 11 feet higher than the first time. The third time he rose, Bibo actually reached the ceiling of the circus tent. Amazingly, the ceiling was 46 feet above the ground. How much farther did Bibo rise the third time?

3. The Crackpot Clowns are a highlight of the circus. The audience is always surprised to see 30 clowns pile into one tiny car: 12 clowns squeeze into the front seat, 11 clowns into the back seat, and 5 into the jump seat. The rest of the clowns fit into the trunk. How many Crackpot Clowns fit into the trunk of the tiny car?

4. The Crackpot Funhouse is filled with crazy mirrors, spinning tunnels, and tilted rooms. One of the crazy mirrors makes people look 2 1/5 feet taller than they really are. When Jimbo Jenkins looked into the mirror, his reflection was 8 7/10 feet tall. What was Jimbo's real height in feet and inches?

Gustov the Amazing Cat
(Using Division to Solve Equations)

Gustov was the most incredible cat in the history of cats. He could do fantastic tricks and terrific stunts.

To learn more about Gustov, read the problems below. Write an equation for each problem, then solve it. When you're done, check your answers.

1. For one of his most famous tricks, Gustov would place some goldfish in his mouth. When he opened his mouth again, there would be 4 times as many goldfish. One night, Gustov opened his mouth at the end of the trick. The audience counted 20 goldfish in his mouth. How many goldfish did Gustov place in his mouth at the start of the trick?

2. One night, Gustov had an anchovy-eating contest with a German shepard named Hans. For every anchovy that Hans ate, Gustov ate 7.5 anchovies. If Gustov ate 45 anchovies, how many did Hans eat?

3. Gustov could juggle longer than any other animal in town. Seymore the Squirrel was also a good juggler, but his record time for juggling was only half as long as Gustov's record. If Seymore's record time for juggling was 6 1/4 minutes, what was Gustov's record time?

4. Using his mouth, Gustov could throw a baseball farther than any other cat. One night, a cat named Jelly challenged Gustov to a throwing contest. In the end, Gustov threw the baseball 24 feet. That was twice as far as Jelly's throw, plus 2 feet. How far did Jelly throw the baseball?

Educational Impressions, Inc.

Lugar the Giant
(Using Division to Solve Equations)

Lugar was one of the giants living in Kinkle Cave. One day, Lugar wandered out of the cave. In the forest, he met a small boy named Brian. Lugar and Brian became good friends, even though they were very different sizes.

Write an equation for each problem, then solve it. When you're done, check your answers.

1. One day, Lugar and Brian used a ruler to compare their heights. They found out that Lugar was 27.3 feet tall, 6.5 times taller than Brian. How tall was Brian?

2. Lugar and Brain liked climbing Kinkle Mountain. They wanted to have a race to see who could climb the fastest, but it wasn't a very fair contest. In the time it took Brian to climb a foot, Lugar could climb 8.5 feet. If Lugar climbed 52.7 feet in a minute, how far did Brian climb in the same amount of time?

3. Lugar and Brian loved skipping rocks on Kinkle Pond. One day, Lugar skipped a rock for 242 feet. That was 4.5 times farther than Brian's rock, plus 3.5 more feet. How far did Brian's rock skip?

4. For Lugar's birthday, Brian wanted to bake a giant cake. He took his mom's favorite cake recipe and tripled each ingredient. For the giant cake, Brian used 9 cups of flour and 2 1/4 cups of sugar. How much flour and sugar did the regular cake recipe call for?

9Y-5, Robot in Training
(Using Multiplication to Solve Equations)

Robot 9Y-5 was the most absent-minded robot at the Galaxy 7 Robot Academy. In spite of his problems, 9Y-5 dreamed of being the next robot selected for a mission into deep space.

Write an equation for each problem, then solve it. When you're done, check your answers.

1. While doing his daily chores at the Robot Academy, 9Y-5 was ironing the space suits of the senior astronauts. When he finished, he turned in the suits to his commander. The commander counted the suits and realized that 54 of them were missing. 9Y-5 blushed and explained that he had burned 1/4 of the suits with the iron. To keep the commander from getting angry, he had launched the burned suits into space. How many suits were there originally?

2. While working in the Academy lunch room, 9Y-5 was baking pot pies. Sadly, he mixed up the salt with the baking powder, and 2 out of 3 pot pies exploded in the oven. If 42 pot pies did not blow up, how many pies was 9Y-5 supposed to make?

3. 9Y-5 was in charge of packing freeze-dried meals for an astronaut traveling to a distant moon. After returning from the moon mission, the astronaut was in a very bad mood. His calculations showed that 9Y-5 had packed only 1/8 of the meals he was supposed to pack. The astronaut had only been given 3 3/4 meals. How many meals should 9Y-5 have packed for the astronaut?

Educational Impressions, Inc.

Nasty Nedra
(Using Multiplication to Solve Equations)

Ever since humans began living in outer space, Nasty Nedra has been known as the meanest girl in the galaxy. Rumors of her evil pranks have spread to every planet. Fed up with her behavior, Nedra's parents sent her to the Dark Side of the Moon School for Young Ladies. Since she arrived at the school, Nedra's been meaner than ever.

Write an equation for each problem, then solve it. When you're done, check your answers.

1. On her first day of school, Nedra placed a sharp moon rock in her teacher's chair. The teacher was not amused. She gave Nedra a piece of paper printed with silver stars. Each time Nedra pulled a prank, the teacher would cross off a star. If all the stars ran out, Nedra would have detention for a year.

    At the end of the first week, Nedra had only 8 stars left. That was just 1/4 of the stars the teacher had given her. How many stars had the teacher given Nedra?

2. Nedra was extra nasty in science class. One day, she snuck some acid out of the chemical cabinet and poured it in her teacher's briefcase. The briefcase was almost completely eaten by the acid. Furious, the teacher made Nedra do an extra science project. For the project, Nedra had to find out exactly how much of the briefcase had been eaten by the acid.

    Nedra examined what was left of the briefcase. The remains weighed only 3/4 of a pound. Nedra's calculations showed that the briefcase had been reduced to 1/16 its original weight. What was the original weight of the briefcase?

3. Nedra really liked playing pranks on the other girls at her school. One afternoon, she sneaked into the Art Room. On the walls were many paintings done by her schoolmates. Using black paint, she began to cover the artwork with her own scribblings. After Nedra had destroyed 2/3 of the paintings, she decided to ruin one more, just for fun. When she was finished, Nedra had destroyed 45 of the paintings. How many paintings were in the room?

Sid the Sorcerer
(Using Proportion to Solve Equations)

Sid had studied for years to become a sorcerer. Finally, he was ready to enter the Annual Sorcerer's Showdown. All the best sorcerers in the land would be there, and the competition was going to be tough.

Write an equation for each problem, then solve it. When you're done, check your answers.

1. Sid practiced extra hard for the Animal Contest. He could change into an average of 12 animals every 60 minutes. At the Showdown, sorcerers would compete to see how many different animals they could change into during a 20-minute period. At the Showdown, Sid performed at a rate proportional to his average. How many animals did he change into during the 20-minute period?

2. At the Showdown, Sid had to cast a spell using frogs. He only knew how to cast spells using frogs with warts. There were 25 frogs to choose from, but only 2 had warts. What percentage of the frogs was Sid able to use for his spell?

3. Sid won first place in the Lemonade Making Contest. Using only 3 gallons of water, he was able to make 18 gallons of lemonade. Another sorcerer, Manto, tied Sid for first place by performing at a proportional rate. Manto started with 5 gallons of water. How much lemonade did Manto make?

4. Sid also did well in the Stick Growing Contest. In 10 minutes, Sid was able to make a stick grow 14 inches. If the stick continued to grow at a proportional rate, how many inches did the stick grow in 30 minutes?

Educational Impressions, Inc.

The Search for Chewing Gum Charlie
(Using Proportion to Solve Equations)

Special Agent Roy is searching for the evil Chewing Gum Charlie. Charlie is known for stealing something, then leaving a wad of chewing gum in its place.

Help Agent Roy find Chewing Gum Charlie. Write an equation for each problem, then solve it. When you're done, check your answers.

1. On Monday, Charlie steals 9 purses and 12 bookbags. Agent Roy has studied Charlie's pattern of crime for years. He knows that Charlie will steal the same ratio of purses to bookbags the next day. On Tuesday, Charlie steals 6 purses. How many bookbags does he steal on Tuesday?

2. On Wednesday, Charlie hits the Corner Mall. He steals the same percentage of items from each store. The CD store has 256 CDs in stock. Charlie steals 16 CDs at the CD store. The bike store has 32 bikes in stock. How many bikes does Charlie steal at the bike store?

3. On Thursday, Charlie steals some popcorn from the Block Cinema. There is enough popcorn in the popper to fill 60 buckets. Charlie steals 12 buckets. What percentage of the popcorn does he steal?

4. On Friday, Agent Roy is hot on Charlie's trail. He knows that Charlie never robs the same store twice. Only 4% of the stores in town have not been robbed by Charlie. There are 75 stores in town. How many stores can Charlie still rob?

Chamber of Parentheses
(Solving Equations with Parentheses)

Dr. Helen Hoogle, Egyptologist, stumbled across an undiscovered chamber inside the Great Pyramid in Egypt. In the chamber, she found an ancient scroll. It contained directions to the hidden treasure of a wealthy Egyptian ruler known as Parentheses the First.

To find the treasure, Dr. Hoogle must solve a series of equations containing parentheses. Here is what the ancient scroll said:

1. Solve the equation below. When you have the answer, travel that many yards toward the northern side of the pyramid.

    $4(2x - 1) = 20$

2. Solve the equation below. When you have the answer, travel that many yards toward the western side of the pyramid.

    $1/2(9k + 1/4) = 18\ 1/8$

3. Solve the equation below. When you have the answer, walk that many steps toward the southeast corner of the pyramid.

    $-7(5c + 11) = -252$

4. Solve the equation below. When you have the answer, dig that many feet into the ground to find the hidden treasure.

    $8\ 2/3 = -2(2\ 1/3 - y)$

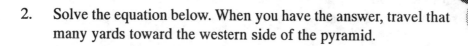

Educational Impressions, Inc.

Sir Bingle
(Solving Equations with Parentheses)

Sir Bingle was one of the bravest knights in the village of Dandle. If anyone could defeat the evil dragon that was destroying the village, it was Sir Bingle. As he prepared for a battle with the dragon, Sir Bingle received an important message from Sid the Sorcerer.

To find out what Sid's message said, solve the equations below.

1. $3(6a + 1) = 39$ $a =$

2. $6(-7c) = -126$ $c =$

3. $4(7e - 19) = 64$ $e =$

4. $-(n - 3) = -1$ $n =$

5. $-2(11r) = -154$ $r =$

6. $-3s(5 - 1) = -12$ $s =$

7. $.5(u - 6) = 1$ $u =$

8. $42 = 5\frac{1}{4}(2 + w)$ $w =$

Now it's time to help Sir Bingle. Use your solutions to decode Sid's message.

Dear Sir Bingle,

When you battle the dragon,
   remember to
   6-5-2-7   1-8-4-1-3-7-5-5-4!

Sincerely,

Sid the Sorcerer

Dr. Kinny & the So. American Butterflies
(Equations with Variables on Both Sides)

Dr. Kinny is an expert on South American butterflies. For nearly ten years, he has lived deep in the Amazon Rain Forest. From his campsite, he watches and records the activities of the jungle butterflies.

During his studies, Dr. Kinny has discovered several butterfly species. Below you'll find his notes. Some of the information is still being calculated.

Species Name	Average Life Span	Average Wingspan
Chessboard	65 days	4.31 inches
Queen Crimson	**x days**	5.2 inches
Hazelnut	154 days	3.9 inches
Red Berry	43 days	4.5 inches
Southern Patch	**y days**	5.2 inches
Tree Chaser	210 days	**n inches**
Leaping Lavender	39 days	1.3 inches
Royal Daisywing	76 days	3.98 inches
Blue Beauty	54 days	**m inches**

1. To calculate the average life span of the Queen Crimson, Dr. Kinny has developed the formula below. Solve the formula to discover the Queen Crimson's average life span.

    $2(x - 6) = -4(x - 45)$, where x = average life span in days

2. Dr. Kinny has also developed a formula for calculating the average wingspan of the Tree Chaser. It is shown below. Use the formula to discover the average wingspan of the Tree Chaser.

    $1/2(12 - n) = 1/3(3n)$, where n = average wingspan in inches

3. Below is another one of Dr. Kinny's formulas. Use it to calculate the average life span of the Southern Patch.

    $2(3y - 1) = 2y + 46$, where y = average life span in days

4. Below is Dr. Kinny's formula for calculating the average wingspan of the Blue Beauty. Use it to find the Blue Beauty's average wingspan.

    $.5(3m) = .25(m + 12.5)$, where m = average wingspan in inches

Educational Impressions, Inc.

Cyndi Snootles' Tree House
(Equation Review)

As everyone knows, Cyndi Snootles is the most spoiled little girl in the world. Whatever Cyndi wants, Cyndi gets. One day, Cyndi decided that she wanted a giant tree house.

1. Cyndi told the tree house designers that she wanted a very big bedroom in her tree house. They built a big bedroom and showed it to Cyndi. She told them it was much too small and that she wanted it twice as big. When the next version was finished, Cyndi said it was still too small. She told the designers to make the bedroom four times bigger than the second version. Finally, Cyndi was happy. Her tree house bedroom was 78 feet wide and 78 feet long.

    How many feet wide and long was the first version of the bedroom?

2. Cyndi also wanted a swimming pool in her tree house. The designers made the pool 24 meters wide and 56 meters long. After the pool was finished, Cyndi decided she wanted 4 dolphins to live in the pool. The pool would have to be bigger, but Cyndi wanted the ratio of the pool's length and width to stay proportional. If the length of the second pool was 84 meters, what was the width of the second pool?

3. Cyndi demanded 8 different entrances to the tree house, each with its own ladder. She also wanted the rungs of the ladders to be solid gold bars. In addition, she wanted each ladder to have the same number of rungs. After some quick calculations, the designers realized that Cyndi's plans required 200 gold bars.

    How many rungs did the designers plan for each ladder to have?

4. By now, Cyndi's tree house was so big, it took 5 trees to hold it up. Cyndi wanted each tree to be decorated with white lights. The designers ordered a total of 3,500 lights. As usual, Cyndi wasn't happy. She wanted each tree to have 500 more lights. If the lights were divided evenly between each tree, how many lights did each tree finally get?

Blipman
(Algebraic Expressions)

Blipman has worked at the Video Palace Arcade since the day it opened. He holds the highest score on every video game in the arcade. Blipman knows more about video games than anyone else in town.

Write an algebraic expression for each question below.

1. Blipman has worked at the Video Palace Arcade for 15 years. How long will he have worked there in x years?

2. Blipman's high score on Space Ape is three times his high score on Castle Crew. If his high score on Castle Crew is n, what is his score on Space Ape?

3. During two games of Neon Nick, Blipman got 7 free lives. If he got x lives in the first game, how many did he get in the second game?

4. Blipman's favorite game is Underwater Wally. During one very good round, Blipman collected 8 anchors, n starfish, and twice as many sharks as starfish. How many objects did he collect during the round?

5. On one crowded Saturday night, 43 more kids came to the arcade than the night before. If z kids came to the arcade the night before, how many came on Saturday night?

6. Blipman makes $7.50 an hour. If he works 10 hours a day, how much does he earn in x days?

7. Wallace is Blipman's favorite opponent. On the game Star Rider, Blipman scored three times as many points as Wallace. If Blipman scored n points, how many points did Wallace score?

8. On Giant Galaxy Mouse, Blipman scored 30 points more than the sum of Wallace's score and Wallace's age. If Wallace's score is s and his age is a, what did Blipman score on Giant Galaxy Mouse?

Educational Impressions, Inc.

Joe Escapades Animal Friends
(Algebraic Expressions)

Ever since Joe Escapade was stranded on a tropical island, he has done his best to be friendly with the local animals. After all, they're the only friends he has.

Write an algebraic expression for each question below.

1. Joe is very friendly with a family of iguanas. He also likes the frogs that hop around his favorite swimming hole. One day, Joe counts 10 more iguanas than frogs. If there are x iguanas, how many frogs are there?

2. There is a warm cave where Joe likes to sleep when it's raining. Inside the cave, he enjoys spending time with 2 friendly wild pigs. Deeper in the cave, there are n unfriendly pigs and 3 times as many man-eating pigs as unfriendly pigs. How many pigs live in the cave?

3. Whenever he can, Joe shares food with his animal friends. One week, Joe picked 9 coconuts and x mangos. If Joe gave his pig friends exactly a third of the food he found that week, how many pieces of fruit did the pigs get?

4. Since Joe has no clocks or calendars on the island, he has to think of special ways to remember his age. This year, the sum of Joe's age and the number of volcanoes on the island is 40. If Joe is n years old, how many volcanoes are on the island?

5. Joe's best friend on the island is a monkey he calls Smiley. Together, Joe and Smiley like to collect seashells on the beach. Joe has twice as many clam shells as the sum of Smiley's conch shells and oyster shells. If Smiley has x conch shells and y oyster shells, how many clam shells does Joe have?

Extra-Practice Sheets

Bigsby's Visitors

During one of his missions in deep space, astronaut Bigsby Booster came upon a strange space-craft. He signaled for the spacecraft to board his ship. Since he hadn't been around any living creatures for months, Bigsby was lonely and needed some company.

As the spacecraft door opened, Bigsby was surprised to see some large aliens with many purple arms. They called themselves Zylorians and said they were from the planet Zylor.

1. That night, Bigsby prepared a big dinner for the Zylorians. As the main course, he made spaghetti with comet sauce. Each alien ate 3 times more helpings than Bigsby. On top of that, each alien decided to eat 4 more helpings. If each alien ate 13 helpings, how many helpings did Bigsby eat?

2. After dinner, Bigsby and the aliens decided to watch a video. Bigsby wanted to serve popcorn to the aliens. However, he didn't have much popcorn on the ship. He had to divide it very carefully. There were 5 aliens on board, and they seemed very hungry. Bigsby decided to give each alien twice as much popcorn as he gave himself. In all, he had 16 1/2 cups of popcorn on the ship. How much popcorn did Bigsby get to eat?

3. While they were watching the video, the Zylorians asked for some soda to wash down the popcorn. Bigsby checked his soda machine. He had 12 liters of Space Fizz. It would be a long time before he could get more soda. After all, he was in deep space. Bigsby decided to share only half of his soda supply with the aliens. If Bigsby divided the soda evenly among the aliens, how much soda did each alien get? (Bigsby decided to drink juice instead of soda.)

4. After the video, each of the aliens had a terrible belly ache. They sent Bigsby to get some stomach medicine. He found a bottle of Tummy Tonic and read the label. It said to use one teaspoon for every 50 pounds of the patient's weight. Bigsby estimated the weight of the aliens and brought them 42 1/2 teaspoons. In his estimation, he used the same weight for each alien. How much did Bigsby estimate that each alien weighed?

Educational Impressions, Inc.

The Swinging Hamsters

The Swinging Hamsters are one of the hottest rock groups in the world. The members of the band—Rip, Rock, Stone, and Crash—are loved by people of all ages. Every record released by the Hamsters goes straight to the top of the charts, and all of their concerts sell out.

1. The Hamsters have their own jet plane for traveling. On one trip, the band flew from New York to Los Angeles. After the first leg of their trip, they stopped for pizza in Detroit. On the next leg of their trip, they traveled twice as far as the first leg. Then they stopped in Denver for hot fudge sundaes. The last leg of their trip was 1,030 miles. If the total distance covered by the band on their trip was 2,680 miles, how many miles was the first leg?

2. The Hamsters love to throw big parties. After one concert, they invited 275 people to a celebration at their mansion. Rip invited 58 people. Rock invited half as many people as Stone. Crash invited twice as many people as Stone. How many people did Stone invite to the party?

3. When they're on tour, the Hamsters are very picky about what they eat. One time, the band ordered some french fries from room service. After they divided the fries evenly, each member got 55 fries. A few minutes later, the band called room service again. They complained that some of the fries were too greasy to eat. They demanded a refund for 44 of the fries. According to the Hamsters, what percentage of the fries were too greasy to eat?

4. The Hamsters love their fans. At each concert, they put a special seal on 5 tickets. After the concert, the special ticket holders get to meet the Hamsters.

   When a concert in Nashville sold out, each ticket holder had a 1 in 4,000 chance of getting a special seal. How many people bought tickets to the concert?

The Monster's Big Date

There once lived a terribly ugly monster. He had purple fur and yellow eyes. When people saw him, they ran away screaming. The monster grew tired of scaring people, and so he moved into an old abandoned castle. He lived in the castle for many years, a very lonely monster.

Then one day, the monster noticed a beautiful young girl in his garden. He walked into the garden, expecting the girl to run away. But instead of running, the girl smiled at the monster. Nervously, he asked her to join him for dinner that night. She agreed. The monster hurried off, wondering how he was going to clean the castle and make dinner by 7 o'clock.

1. First, the monster had to tidy up his giant castle. Every room was filled with dust and cobwebs. The monster looked at his watch. It was noon. He had to start cooking dinner by 6 o'clock. If he spent 15 minutes cleaning each room of the castle, he could finish in time. How many rooms were in the castle?

2. The monster didn't want the castle to seem dark or scary. He needed some candles to brighten up the place. He knew exactly how many candles he needed for the library. He would need twice as many candles for the living room as he did for the library. Also, he would need half as many candles for the foyer as he did for the living room. The monster called a local candle maker and ordered 64 candles. How many candles did the monster need for the library?

3. Once the castle was clean and bright, the monster could focus on dinner. He was making pasta salad and chocolate cake for dessert. The pasta salad recipe called for 5 1/2 cups of pasta noodles. That made enough salad for 8 people, but the monster only needed enough salad for 2 people. How many cups of pasta noodles did he need to use?

Educational Impressions, Inc.

Felix, the Generous Great White Shark

Felix was known as the kindest, most generous shark in the entire Atlantic Ocean. He would share his food with any creature, large or small.

1. One morning, Felix collected some stalks of seaweed from the ocean floor. He knew he was supposed to eat smaller fish like the other sharks, but most of the fish were his friends. He couldn't bare to eat them. Felix ate 4 of the seaweed stalks for lunch. He also gave 6 to Harry the Eel, 7 to Barney the Barracuda, and 3 to Jimmy the Grouper. At the end of the day, Felix had 1/3 of the seaweed stalks he had collected that morning. How many stalks had Felix collected that morning?

2. In his spare time, Felix collected things that fell to the bottom of the ocean. He shared the treasures with his best friend, Marty the Marlin. One day, Felix found 8 wrist watches, some sunglasses, and four times as many rings as sunglasses. When he added the watches, sunglasses and rings together, Felix realized he had found 33 things that day. How many rings did Felix find that day?

3. One afternoon, Felix found the best treasure he had ever seen. It was a shiny bracelet with 42 diamonds. He gave one diamond to his mother, one to Marty, and one to each of his brothers. In all, Felix gave away half of the diamonds on the bracelet. How many brothers did Felix have?

4. Whenever Felix lost a shark tooth, he gave it away as a token of good luck. One year, he lost 32 teeth. He gave 25% of his lost teeth to Marty, 50% to his favorite brother, and the rest to a starfish who was just passing through. How many teeth did Felix give the starfish?

Mr. Sippy's Sandwich Sale

Mr. Sippy owned Sippy's Sandwich Shop. The shop offered a bigger variety of sandwiches than any other place in town. Some of the sandwiches were more popular than others. Mr. Sippy wanted to clean out his freezer and get rid of the unpopular sandwiches. He decided to have a huge Sandwich Sale.

1. Mr. Sippy normally sold the Olive, Ketchup, and Cheese Sandwich for $2.75. During the sale, it was reduced by $0.55. What was the percentage of the discount on the Olive, Ketchup, and Cheese Sandwich?

2. The Sippy Deluxe Sandwich, made with peanut butter and mayonnaise, was not very popular either. Mr. Sippy decided to sell it for 50% off. Then he lowered the price even more. He offered the sandwich at an additional 20% off the reduced price. That lowered the price of the Sippy Deluxe Sandwich to $0.76. How much was the Sippy Deluxe Sandwich originally?

3. Mr. Sippy's most unpopular sandwich was the Chocolate and Onion Melt. Originally, it sold for $3.24. Mr. Sippy reduced the price to 1/3 of its original price. Then he added 15% to cover the high cost of chocolate. What was the new sale price of the Chocolate and Onion Melt? Round your answer to the nearest penny.

4. Mr. Sippy decided to offer a soup and sandwich combo during the sale. He lowered the price of the Carrot and Raisin Burger by 30%. He then added a bowl of Oyster Stew. The stew was normally $2.10 a bowl. Mr. Sippy lowered the price of the soup by 20%, making the soup and sandwich combo just $4.27. What was the original price of the Carrot and Raisin Burger?

Educational Impressions, Inc.

The Giant Pizza

Miguel is trying to break a world record by making a pizza that is 60 feet wide. To do it, he needs lots of ingredients and some good algebra skills. He must convert the ingredients of a regular-sized pizza into the proportions needed for his giant pizza.

1. For a regular-sized pizza, Miguel would need 1 1/4 cups tomato sauce. For his giant pizza, he needs 40 times that amount. Instead of having to measure out all those cups, Miguel can convert the amount needed into gallons. One gallon equals 16 cups. How many gallons of pizza sauce does Miguel need? Express your answer as a mixed number.

2. Miguel is making a pepperoni pizza. For the regular-sized pizza, he would need 35 slices of pepperoni. For the giant pizza, he will need 40 times that amount. One pound of pepperoni yields 40 slices. How many pounds of pepperoni will Miguel need for his pizza?

3. For the giant pizza crust, Miguel needs 52 pounds of flour. He knows that 2 1/2 cups of flour equals one pound. How many cups of flour would Miguel need for the regular-sized pizza? (HINT: Remember, to make the giant pizza, Miguel is increasing the regular-sized pizza recipe by 40 times.)

4. Miguel also needs water for the pizza crust. For the regular-sized pizza, he would need 10 tablespoons. For the giant pizza, he will need 25 cups of water. How many tablespoons does it take to make one cup?

The Great Storm

On the night of November 15, 1902, the town of Polkville had the worst storm anyone had ever seen.

1. During the first hour of the storm, it rained .4 inches. During the second hour of the storm, it rained three times that much. During the third hour of the storm, it rained twice as much as it had in the first two hours. The storm lasted exactly four hours. The total rainfall during the storm was 7.5 inches. How many inches did it rain during the fourth hour of the storm?

2. Mrs. Nell Mae was very interested in lightning. She kept track of each lightning bolt produced by the big storm. During the first two hours, she counted 230 bolts. During the fourth hour, she counted enough bolts to equal exactly 80% of the bolts from the third hour. At the end of the storm, she found that an average of 107 bolts had struck Polkville during each hour of the storm. How many bolts did she record in the third hour of the storm?

3. Mr. Flip and Mr. Brap always fought over who had the best lawn. In fact, they competed with each other about everything. After the storm, Mr. Flip collected 48 hail stones from his lawn. Mr. Flip's lawn covered 64 square yards. Mr. Brap was frustrated to find only 42 hail stones in his lawn. If the hail stones fell proportionately on both lawns, how many square yards did Mr. Brap's lawn cover?

4. Mr. Craggle at the Country Store was watching the thermometer during the storm. He first looked at the thermometer when the storm hit at 1 p.m. An hour later, the temperature had dropped 4 degrees. After another hour, it had dropped 3 more degrees. Another hour later, it had dropped 1 more degree. Another hour later, it had risen 2 degrees. The average of the last four hourly temperatures was 55.75 degrees. What temperature did Mr. Craggle see on thermometer at 1 p.m.?

Educational Impressions, Inc.

Jamal's Trip to the Big City

Jamal's family had been planning a trip to Greatropolis for weeks. Jamal had never been to such a large city before, and he was very excited. He'd been saving his allowance for weeks.

1. The family's first stop in Greatropolis was Biggy's, the largest department store in the world. Jamal had $147.50 to spend on the entire trip. At Biggy's, he found a hat for $24 and a Greatropolis T-shirt that he really liked. If Jamal had bought the T-shirt and the hat, he would have spent 30% of his money. How much was the T-shirt?

2. The next day, Jamal's family went to the Greatropolis Zoo. Jamal wanted to buy some fish to feed the seals. There were 8 fish to a pack, and each pack cost $2.75. Jamal bought enough fish for each seal to have one. He spent $13.75 on the fish. How many seals were at the zoo?

3. After the zoo, Jamal's family decided to visit the Greatropolis Museum of Natural History. Jamal really liked the dinosaur bones at the museum. At the gift shop, he decided to buy a small model of the Tyrannosaurus Rex bones. The model was marked down 30%, and tax was 10% of the discount price. Jamal paid $13.09 for the model. How much was the model originally?

4. On their last day in Greatropolis, Jamal and his family went ice skating in Midtown Park. It cost $3.25 for each family member to get into the ice rink, plus the cost of skate rentals. There were five people in Jamal's family, and everyone skated. If the family spent $30 on ice skating, what was the rental cost for each pair of skates?

The Doofies vs. the Banktown Bullwhips

The Doverville Doofies have never won a football game, but that hasn't stopped them from trying. This year, when they played the Banktown Bullwhips, they gave it their best shot.

1. In the first quarter, the Doofies' quarterback threw 5 interceptions. In the second quarter, he threw even more interceptions. In the third and fourth quarters, he threw a total of twice as many interceptions as he'd thrown in the second quarter. In all, the quarterback threw 29 interceptions during the game against the Bullwhips. How many interceptions were thrown in the second quarter?

2. During the game, the Bullwhips completed 80% of their passes. The receivers caught 48 passes. How many passes were thrown during the game?

3. The Bullwhips scored 5 field goals at 3 points each, twice as many touchdowns as field goals at 6 points each, and several extra points at 1 point each. The final score of the game was 78 to 0. How many extra points did the Bullwhips score?

4. The coach for the Doofies keeps a lucky number written on a piece of paper in his pocket. Even though the number hasn't been very lucky for the team, he still believes that it will work someday. When a player asked the coach what the lucky number was, the coach wouldn't say. Instead, he gave the player a clue. He said, "Half of the number is 10 less than triple the number." What is the lucky number?

Educational Impressions, Inc.

Solutions

REVIEW SHEETS

What's an Equation? (Page 8)
1. y
2. 1/2
3. Two should be added to both sides.
4. Seven should be added to both sides.

Working With Variables (Page 9)
1. $8x$
2. $31x$
3. $15x^2$
4. 4
5. $52x$
6. $4x$
7. $5x$
8. $20/x$

Using Addition to Solve Equations (Page 10)
1. $c = 55$
2. $y = 3$
3. $s = 12$
4. $z = 1$
5. $m = 9$

Using Subtraction to Solve Equations (Page 11)
1. $j = 55$
2. $x = 6$
3. $k = 2.3$
4. $y = 2/4$ or $1/2$
5. $m = -23$

Using Division to Solve Equations (Page 12)
1. $z = 3$
2. $m = 6$
3. $k = 4$
4. $y = 8$
5. $c = 18$

Using Multiplication to Solve Equations (Page 13)
1. $z = 3$
2. $x = 4$
3. $c = 5$
4. $b = 1$
5. $x = 4$

Combining Like Terms (Page 14)
1. $12x = 12$, $x = 1$
2. $8 = 2c$, $c = 4$
3. $8y = 32$, $y = 4$
4. $6z = 12$, $z = 2$
5. $3n = 36$, $n = 12$
6. $-2 = -6y$, $y = 1/3$
7. $x = 16\ 1/2$
8. $1.75m = 8.75$, $m = 5$

Equations with Fractions (Page 15)
1. 7/12
2. 3/10
3. 1/15
4. 2/3
5. 2 2/3
6. 2 1/3
7. 1/3
8. 4 1/2

Extra Review: Equations with Fractions (Page 16)
1. $x = 4$
2. $x = 1/2$
3. $x = 1\ 1/8$
4. $x = 3/10$
5. $x = 20$
6. $x = 1/5$
7. $x = 3$
8. $x = 1\ 1/4$
9. $x = 3/8$
10. $x = 3/10$

Equations with Parentheses (Page 17)

1. $4x - 20$
2. $6x + 21$
3. $21c + 91$
4. $5a$
5. $2.88z + 4.8$
6. $24y - 8$
7. $40 - 16x$
8. $b - 1/8$

Extra Review: Equations with Parentheses (Page 18)

1. $x = 2$
2. $x = 4$
3. $x = 9$
4. $x = 3$
5. $x = 9$
6. $x = 11$
7. $x = 4.5$
8. $x = 6$
9. $x = 5$
10. $x = 1/2$

Equations with Positive and Negative Numbers (Page 19)

1. -21
2. 16
3. -32
4. 6
5. -5
6. 60
7. -12
8. 3
9. -91
10. -13

Extra Review: Equations with Positive and Negative Numbers (Page 20)

1. $x = 12$
2. $x = 8$
3. $x = 65$
4. $x = 6$
5. $x = 5.5$
6. $x = 1/2$
7. $x = -1/2$
8. $x = 16.5$
9. $x = -1$
10. $x = 5$

Writing Algebraic Expressions (Page 21)

1. $5 + 4$
2. $2 + 6$
3. $12 - 6$
4. $-8 + 3$
5. 4×-2
6. $x + 5$
7. $8y + 9$
8. $2x - 3$
9. $5z + x$
10. $1/2y - 18$

Extra Review: Writing Algebraic Expressions (Page 22)

1. $12 + x$
2. $24 - y$
3. $m - 6$
4. $n + 20$
5. $168 - y$
6. $6x$
7. $(b + f) + 5$
8. $w = 2h$

Writing Equations for Word Problems (Page 23)
(NOTE: Some equations can be written more than one way.)

1. $31 + n = 48$
2. $89 - y = 67$
3. $1/2n + 5 = 21$
4. $m = 3s$
5. $n = b - 3$
6. $11 + 1/2n = 77$
7. $.4y = 48$
8. $(4 + 20) z = 144$

Educational Impressions, Inc.

Extra Review: Writing Equations for Word Problems (Page 24)
(NOTE: Some equations can be written more than one way.)

1. $21 - n = 14$
   $n = 7$

2. $2x + 12 = 102$
   $x = 45$

3. $4 + 1/3y = 34$
   $y = 90$

4. $.15z = 24$
   $z = 160$

5. $3(4 + c) = 30$
   $c = 6$

6. $y/14 = 6$
   $y = 84$

7. $54 + m = 54$
   $m = 0$

8. $5 + 1/4j = 21$
   $j = 64$

Equations with Variables on Both Sides (Page 25)
(NOTE: Some equations can be written more than one way.)

1. $m + 1 = 4(1/2m)$
2. $4x = x - 2$
3. $3k = 2k - 12$
4. $r + 1/2 = 6r$

5. $32 + c = 1/2c$
6. $n = 1/3(n + 18)$
7. $2j = 3j + 3$
8. $1/2b = 2b - 10$

Extra Review: Equations with Variables on Both Sides (Page 26)
(NOTE: Some equations can be written more than one way.)

1. $1/2k = 3k + 5$
   $k = -2$

2. $d = 1/3(d + 36)$
   $d = 18$

3. $2n = 3n - 5$
   $n = 5$

4. $y/2 = 2y - 18$
   $y = 12$

5. $16 + c = 1/2c$
   $c = -32$

6. $3x = x - 12$
   $x = -6$

7. $12 + m = 4m/2$
   $m = 12$

8. $z + 1/2 = 3z$
   $z = 1/4$

Using Proportion to Solve Equations (Page 27)

1. $z = 1$
2. $k = 12$
3. $y = 10$

4. $a = 4$
5. $x = 12$

Extra Review: Using Proportion to Solve Equations (Page 28)

1. $19/38 = x/100$
   50%

2. $33/55 = x/100$
   60%

3. $3/4 = x/100$
   75%

4. $4/12 = x/18$
   6 categories

5. $2/6 = 3/x$
   9 family members

6. $60/100 = 51/x$
   85 baskets

Extra Review: Solving Equations (Page 29)

1. $y = 4$
2. $y = -28$
3. $y = 6$
4. $y = 0$
5. $y = 7.1$
6. $y = 1/2$
7. $y = 9.5$
8. $y = 2\,1/2$
9. $y = 3.9$
10. $y = -.5$ (or $-1/2$)

11. $x = 1$
12. $x = 0$
13. $x = 2$
14. $x = -7$
15. $x = -3$
16. $x = 5$
17. $x = 21$
18. $x = 2$
19. $x = 10$
20. $x = 6$

Educational Impressions, Inc.

SKILL-BUILDER SHEETS

Wilheim's Wax Museum: Using Addition to Solve Equations (Page 32)

1. $x - 9 = 68$
   $x = 77$ gallons
2. $342 - x = 256$
   $x = 86$ gallons
3. $x - 6\ 1/2 = 67\ 1/4$
   $x = 73\ 3/4$ gallons
4. $x - .6 - 1.5 = 39.4$
   $x = 41.5$ gallons

Count Dimula: Using Addition to Solve Equations (Page 33)

1. $23 - x = 18$
   $x = 5$ undershirts
2. $x - 8 = 214$
   $x = 222$ mice
3. $x - 1\ 7/8 = 3\ 1/4$
   $x = 5\ 1/8$ cans

S.S. Rainey: Using Subtraction to Solve Equations (Page 34)

1. $x + 13 = 32$
   $x = 19$ pools
2. $x + 6 + 7 = 32$
   $x = 19$ anchors
3. $87 + x = 212$
   $x = 125$ sharks
4. $x + 40\ 1/2 = 82\ 2/3$
   $x = 42\ 1/6$ gallons

The Crackpot Circus: Using Subtraction to Solve Equations (Page 35)

1. $x + 30\ 1/2 = 324\ 2/3$
   $x = 294\ 1/6$ yards
2. $17 + 11 + x = 46$
   $x = 18$ feet
3. $12 + 11 + 5 + x = 30$
   $x = 2$ clowns
4. $x + 2\ 1/5 = 8\ 7/10$
   $x = 6\ 1/2$ feet or 6 feet, 6 inches

Gustov the Amazing Cat: Using Division to Solve Equations (Page 36)

1. $4x = 20$
   $x = 5$ goldfish
2. $7.5x = 45$
   $x = 6$ anchovies
3. $1/2x = 6\ 1/4$
   $x = 12\ 1/2$ minutes
4. $2x + 2 = 24$
   $x = 11$ feet

Lugar the Giant: Using Division to Solve Equations (Page 37)

1. $6.5x = 27.3$
   $x = 4.2$ feet
2. $8.5x = 52.7$
   $x = 6.2$ feet
3. $4.5x + 3.5 = 242$
   $x = 53$ feet
4. $3x = 9$
   $x = 3$ cups of flour
   $3x = 2\ 1/4$
   $x = 3/4$ cup of sugar

9Y-5, Robot in Training: Using Multiplication to Solve Equations (Page 38)

1. $1/4\ x = 54$
   $x = 216$ suits
2. $1/3\ x = 42$
   $x = 126$ pies
3. $1/8\ x = 3\ 3/4$
   $x = 30$ meals

Educational Impressions, Inc.

Nasty Nedra: Using Multiplication to Solve Equations (Page 39)
1. $1/4\,x = 8$
   $x = 32$ stars
2. $1/16\,x = 3/4$
   $x = 12$ pounds
3. $2/3\,x + 1 = 45$
   $x = 66$ paintings

Sid the Sorcerer: Using Proportion to Solve an Equation (Page 40)
1. $12/60 = x/20$
   $x = 4$ animals
2. $2/25 = x/100$
   $x = 8\%$
3. $3/18 = 5/x$
   $x = 30$ gallons
4. $10/14 = 30/x$
   $x = 42$ inches

The Search for Chewing Gum Charlie: Using Proportion to Solve an Equation (Page 41)
1. $9/12 = 6/x$
   $x = 8$ bookbags
2. $16/256 = x/32$
   $x = 2$ bikes
3. $12/60 = x/100$
   $x = 20\%$
4. $x/75 = 4/100$
   $x = 3$ stores

Chamber of Parentheses: Solving Equations with Parentheses (Page 42)
1. $x = 3$ yards
2. $k = 4$ yards
3. $c = 5$ steps
4. $y = 6\ 2/3$ feet

Sir Bingle: Solving Equations with Parentheses (Page 43)
1. $a = 2$
2. $c = 3$
3. $e = 5$
4. $n = 4$
5. $r = 7$
6. $s = 1$
7. $u = 8$
8. $w = 6$
The decoded message is "wear sunscreen."

Dr. Kinny and the South American Butterflies: Equations with Variables on Both Sides (Page 44)
1. $x = 32$ days
2. $n = 4$ inches
3. $y = 12$ days
4. $m = 2.5$ inches

Cyndi Snootles' Tree House: Equation Review (Page 45)
1. 9.75 feet each
2. 36 meters
3. 25 rungs
4. 1,200 lights

Blipman: Algebraic Expressions (Page 46)
1. $15 + x$
2. $3n$
3. $7 - x$
4. $8 + n + 2n$
5. $z + 43$
6. $7.5\,(10x)$
7. $1/3n$
8. $(s + a) + 30$

Joe Escapade's Animal Friends: Algebraic Expressions (Page 47)
1. $x - 10$
2. $2 + n + 3n$
3. $1/3\,(9 + x)$
4. $40 - n$
5. $2\,(x + y)$

EXTRA-PRACTICE SHEETS

Bigsby's Visitors (Page 50)
1. 3 helpings
2. 1 1/2 cups
3. 1.2 liters
4. 425 pounds

The Swinging Hamsters (Page 51)
1. 550 miles
2. 62 people
3. 20% of the fries
4. 20,000 people

The Monster's Big Date (Page 52)
1. 24 rooms
2. 16 candles
3. 1 3/8 cups of pasta noodles

Felix, the Generous Great White Shark (Page 53)
1. 30 stalks
2. 20 rings
3. 19 brothers
4. 8 teeth

Mr. Sippy's Sandwich Sale (Page 54)
1. 20%
2. $1.90
3. $1.24
4. $3.70

The Giant Pizza (Page 55)
1. 3 1/8 gallons pizza sauce
2. 35 pounds pepperoni
3. 3 1/4 cups flour
4. 16 tablespoons water

The Great Storm (Page 56)
1. 2.7 inches
2. 110 bolts
3. 56 square yards
4. 62 degrees

Jamal's Trip to the Big City (Page 57)
1. $20.25
2. 40 seals
3. $17
4. $2.75

The Doofies vs. the Banktown Bullwhips (Page 58)
1. 8 interceptions
2. 60 passes
3. 3 extra points
4. 4

Educational Impressions, Inc.